Nice Words Matter

Written by Diane Stinson
Illustrated by Nicolas Peruzzo

To: Joshua I hope you have fun with friends like Jack and Sophie, riding bikes, swinging on swings and using nice words! Happy Reading! Diane Stinson

ISBN 978-1-61225-366-4

Published by Mirror Publishing
Fort Payne, Alabama 35967

Printed in the USA.

Dedicated to my mother and my husband, the nicest people I have ever known.

Also dedicated to my granddaughter, Meredith and my children, the keepers of my heart.

This is Sophie. Sophie is a very happy little girl. Sophie loves her home and her family.

Sophie loves her pets, Cheeto (the puppy) and Ziti (the kitten). Sophie loves her friend Jack. Jack lives next door to Sophie.

Sophie and Jack play everyday. Sophie and Jack take turns pushing each other on the swing. Jack and Sophie ride bikes and play in the tree house.

Today Sophie came home sad and didn't want to play with Jack anymore. Jack doesn't know why Sophie won't play today. Now Jack is sad too.

Sophie sat with her daddy. Sophie's daddy asked her why she was so sad and why she didn't want to swing today with Jack.

Sophie told her daddy, "Jack said I'm dumb. Am I?"
"Of course not," said Sophie's daddy. Sophie's daddy told
her he thought Jack had just made a mistake.

Sophie's daddy told her that sometimes mean words hurt as much as a boo boo. Sophie told her daddy she felt like she had a boo boo on her heart.

Sophie didn't feel like it was a mistake. Sophie felt sad. Sophie went to swing on the tire swing next to the tree house alone.

Jack asked if he could play.
Sophie said, "No, thank you."
Jack started to walk home.

Sophie's daddy saw Jack leave. Sophie's daddy said "hello" to Jack. Jack told Sophie's daddy that he was sad that Sophie didn't want to play with him.

Sophie's daddy told Jack he had hurt Sophie's feelings when he told her she was dumb.

Jack thought for a moment. Jack remembered saying she was dumb when he asked what her favorite color was and she said pink, which he thought was dumb because blue is so much better. Jack told Sophie's daddy he didn't mean to hurt Sophie.

Sophie's daddy told Jack that sometimes words hurt, especially when they come from a friend.

Jack thought about Sophie on his way home. Jack looked all around his room for a way to tell Sophie he was sorry. He thought about things that Sophie liked.

Finally, Jack saw his crayons. Jack took the pink crayon out of the box. Jack began to draw a big circle.

Jack looked out his window and saw Sophie on the swing. Jack folded the paper and put it in his pocket. Jack had a wonderful surprise for Sophie.

Jack told Sophie he was very sorry. Jack said he wanted her to be happy again and he didn't think she was dumb. Jack told Sophie what her daddy told him about words hurting.

Jack gave Sophie the folded piece of paper and told her again that he was sorry. Sophie unfolded the paper and saw a big bright pink happy face. Sophie smiled just like the drawing and so did her heart.

Sophie and Jack learned words can sometimes hurt. Sophie and Jack promised to use nice words from now on with everybody.

Sophie and Jack are best friends forever.

CPSIA information can be obtained at www.ICGtesting.com
Printed in the USA
BVIW12n1346060317
477676BV00001B/4